Tom and Ricky

and the

Oil Well Mystery

Bob Wright

High Noon Books
Novato, California

The Oil Well Mystery

Bob Wright
AR B.L.: 2.2
Points: 0.5   UG

Cover Design: Nancy Peach
Illustrations: Herb Heidinger

Glossary: barrel, shoes, station, trunk

International Standard Book Number: 0-87879-367-4

10 09 08 07 06 05 04 03
15 14 13 12 11 10

You'll enjoy all the High Noon Books.
Write for a free full list of titles.

Contents

CHAPTER 1

An Oil Change

It was Saturday morning. Everyone was busy at Ricky's house. It was a good day.

"Ricky! Where are you?" Ricky's dad called.

"I'm here in the house," Ricky called back.

"Will you give me a hand? I need some help," his dad called back.

Ricky went outside to find out what his dad wanted. "What's up?" he asked.

"I'm changing the oil in the car. Give me a hand," his dad said.

1

"OK. What do you want me to do?" Ricky asked.

"When I get under the car, hand me that big pan," his dad said.

Ricky's dad got under the car. "OK. I'm ready," he said.

Ricky pushed the big pan to him. The oil started to run out into the pan. Just then Tom rode up on his bike.

"What's doing, Tom?" Ricky asked.

"Want to go fishing with me?" Tom asked.

"I'm helping my dad change the oil," Ricky said.

"Do you need any help?" Tom asked.

"No. Not right now," Ricky said.

Ricky's dad got out from under the car. "I have to let all that dirty oil out. It's about time. I haven't changed the oil in a long time," he said.

Ricky's dad got an old rag. He had oil all over his hands. "That's a dirty job," he said as he wiped off the oil.

"What do you think, Ricky? Can you go?" Tom asked.

Ricky looked at his dad. "What about it? Will you need me?" he asked.

"No. I'll have to let the oil run out. It's OK. You can go. But don't stay long. I'll need you later on," his dad said.

"Let me get my fishing pole. Then we'll head on over to the creek," Ricky said.

He ran into the house. Then he came back with his pole.

Patches started to bark.

"OK. OK. You can come with us," Ricky said.

Ricky's dad called out, "Don't forget, Ricky. I'll need you. We have to take that dirty oil down to Tim's gas station,"

"Tim's gas station?" Tom said.

"Yes. My dad buys the new oil there. Then Tim lets him take the old oil there. That way my dad doesn't have to get rid of it himself," Ricky said.

Tom and Ricky started off on their bikes. Patches ran along with them to the creek.

CHAPTER 2

Where Are The Fish?

No one else was at the creek. Tom and Ricky had it all to themselves. Patches ran right down to the creek. He started to bark. Then he jumped into the water.

"Patches! Patches! Come here," Ricky called.

Patches came back out of the water.

"Sit down. You'll make all the fish go away with that barking," Ricky said. Patches sat down and didn't move.

"Look at Patches. What does he have all over him?" Tom asked.

Ricky looked at Patches. "Boy, he's dirty," he said.

Patches looked all brown.

"The creek must be dirty. Come on. Let's see what's up," Ricky said.

They walked over to the creek. The water seemed to shine when they looked at it.

"There's something in the creek. Look at the way the water shines," Tom said.

"Maybe it's nothing. Let's see if we can catch some fish," Ricky said.

They put their fish lines into the water. They waited. But the fish weren't biting.

"How are you doing?" Tom asked.

"Not a thing. How about you?" Ricky asked.

Ricky took the line in his hand. "Boy, this feels funny."

"I haven't had a bite. Nothing," Tom answered.

"Let's go a little more up the creek. Maybe we'll have some luck up that way," Ricky said.

They took their lines out of the water.

"Ricky! Look at your line. It's dirty. There's something all over it," Tom said.

"Yours, too," Ricky said.

Ricky took the line in his hand. "Boy, this feels funny," he said.

"You're not kidding. Mine feels the same way. What could it be?" Tom asked.

"Wait. This looks like oil!" Ricky said.

"Oil? You're kidding. How could it be oil?" Tom asked.

"No. I think it is. That's what made the creek shine. Oil stays on the top of water. That's what we saw in the creek," Ricky said.

"That's why there aren't any fish here," Tom said.

"That's right. The oil would kill them," Ricky said.

"But where is the oil coming from?" Tom asked.

"You've got me," Ricky answered.

"Well, come on. Let's go up the creek. Maybe there won't be any oil up that way," Tom said.

"And maybe the fish will be biting," Ricky said.

"What about our bikes. Should we take them?" Tom asked.

"No. Let's leave them here. They'll be OK," Ricky said.

Tom and Ricky walked along the creek. Patches walked along with them.

"How about this place?" Tom asked.

Ricky walked over to the creek. He looked into the water. "No. It's still dirty. This place has oil in it, too," Ricky said.

Tom looked up to where an old road was. "What's that thing up on the hill?" he asked.

"What?" Ricky asked.

"That thing up there," Tom said.

Ricky looked up the hill.

"Oh, that. My dad told me about that. Years ago Mr. Stone thought there was oil in the ground. He started to make that oil well," Ricky said.

"Did he find any oil?" Tom asked.

"No. So he stopped making the oil well," Ricky said.

Ricky stopped. He looked at Tom.

"Do you think the oil in the creek is from that well? Maybe there is oil in the ground," Tom said.

"That oil in the creek has to be coming from somewhere," Ricky said.

"That means Mr. Stone could be a rich man if the oil is from there," Tom said.

CHAPTER 3

More Oil

Tom and Ricky looked at Mr. Stone's old oil well. Then they looked back into the creek.

"It's no use to try to fish. The oil has killed the fish," Tom said.

Ricky looked at his watch. "And I have to get back home. I told my dad I would help him," Ricky said.

They started back to their bikes.

"Are we the only ones who have seen the oil in the creek?" Tom asked.

"We must be. No one else has said anything about oil here," Ricky said.

"Not many people come here to fish. Maybe that's why," Tom said.

They got back to their bikes. Then they started back home. Patches ran along with them.

Ricky's dad saw them coming. "Look at Patches. Where has he been?" he asked.

"He ran into the creek," Ricky answered.

"The creek? Is that how he got dirty? And look at your shoes. What do you have all over them?"

"It's oil," Tom said.

"Oil? At the creek?" Ricky's dad asked.

"Well, we think it's oil," Ricky said.

Ricky's dad bent down. He looked at their shoes. Then he said, "It sure is oil. That's funny. Oil in the creek?"

"We think it's coming from that old well. That's the one you told me about. It's the one Mr. Stone made," Ricky said.

"That's right. I forgot about that old well. It was a long time ago. Mr. Stone thought there was oil there. He thought he would become very rich," Ricky's dad said.

"What do you think about it?" Ricky asked.

"Right now we have to get rid of the oil from the car. Wipe that oil off your shoes. Then we'll go over to Tim's gas station," he answered.

"OK," Ricky said.

Ricky's dad gave them an old rag. They wiped the oil off their shoes.

"Ready?" Ricky's dad asked.

"We sure are," Ricky answered.

"I have the old oil in that big can. Help me get it into the car," he said.

Tom and Ricky got the old can. They put it in the trunk.

Patches started to bark. He knew they were going somewhere.

"OK. OK. Take that rag. Get the oil off him. He can go, too," Ricky's dad said.

Ricky wiped the oil off. Then Patches jumped in the car with all of them.

CHAPTER 4

The Gas Station

Tim's gas station was near Ricky's house. It didn't take long to get there. Ricky's dad pulled in and stopped the car.

A man started to come over to the car.

"Is that Tim?" Ricky asked.

"No. I don't see Tim here," Ricky's dad answered.

"Hi. Can I help you?" the man said.

"Yes. I'm looking for Tim," Ricky's dad said.

"Tim doesn't own this gas station any more," the man said.

"Where is Tim?" Ricky's dad asked.

"He sold the station to me. He moved away. My name is Bob," the man said.

"Tim used to let me bring my old oil here," Ricky's dad said.

"That's right. Tim told me about that. A lot of people buy new oil from us. We still let them bring their old oil here. Do you have any you want to leave off?" Bob asked.

"I sure do," Ricky's dad answered.

"You can put it right over there. See those four big barrels? Just put it in one of them," Bob said.

Then he went over to talk to another man.

"We'll get the old oil out of the trunk,"
Ricky said.

Tom and Ricky put the oil in one of the barrels.

Tom and Ricky got out of the car. Ricky's dad opened the trunk. They carried the can over to the barrels.

"Which one should we use?" Tom called out.

Bob heard them talking. "Use any one you want. They are all pretty full," he said.

Tom and Ricky put the old oil in one of the barrels.

Then Ricky said, "Why does Bob let people bring their old oil here?"

"Bob is like Tim. A lot of people in town buy new oil here. Tim used to sell a lot of oil. It helps people when they can get rid of their old oil," his dad said.

Bob came over to them. "Is there anything you need?" he said.

"I might as well get some gas," Ricky's dad said.

He got gas into the car. Then he paid Bob.

"Come back again," Bob said.

"We'll see you soon," Ricky's dad said.

"That was fast," Ricky said.

"Now we'll go back home," Ricky's dad said.

"Wait. We're near the creek. Take us over there. We want to show you what the creek looks like," Ricky said.

"That's a good idea. I want to see what that's all about," his dad said.

CHAPTER 5

Mr. Stone's Oil Well

The creek was close to Bob's gas station. Ricky's dad didn't even have to get on Front Street.

"You can stop the car here," Ricky said.

"Boy, we got here fast," Tom said.

"We sure did. This part of the creek is very close to the gas station," Ricky's dad answered.

They all got out of the car. Patches started to bark. He knew the creek very well.

"Look, Dad. There it is. That's Mr. Stone's old oil well, isn't it?" Ricky asked.

"Yes. That's it. And still right close to this old road. A lot of people don't use this old road any more. That's why people forgot it was still here," Ricky's dad said.

"Come on down to the creek. We'll show you the oil in it," Ricky said.

"I haven't been down to the creek in years and years," Ricky's dad said.

They all went down the hill to the creek. Ricky's dad looked all around.

"You're right. There is oil in the creek. The oil seems to be coming down the hill. It's coming from Mr. Stone's well, I think," he said.

"That's why all those fish were killed," Ricky said.

"Look over here. The water here is clean," Tom said.

"And I can see fish over there," Ricky said.

"The oil is coming out here. Then it goes into the creek. That's why the fish down the creek are being killed," Ricky's dad said.

"But what about the oil? Do you think there might really be a lot here in the ground?" Ricky asked.

"It seems to be coming down the hill from the well," Tom said.

"But there isn't a lot of it," Ricky said.

"Let's go back up the hill. Try to see where it's coming from," Ricky's dad said.

"OK. Let's go," Ricky said.

They all walked slowly back up the hill. Patches was right in back of them. They could see where the oil had run down the hill.

"Look. It stops here," Tom said.

"That's close to the well," Ricky said.

"Maybe Mr. Stone was close to the oil, but not close enough," Ricky's dad said.

"What should we do now?" Ricky asked.

"I think we should talk to Sergeant Collins," Ricky's dad said.

"Why Sergeant Collins?" Tom asked.

"Having oil in the creek is not good. And, a fire could start from that oil well," Ricky's dad said.

"That's right," Tom said.

"What if there really is a lot of oil here?" Ricky asked.

"I don't even know who owns all this land," Ricky's dad said.

"You mean Mr. Stone wouldn't be rich?" Ricky asked.

"Mr. Stone made that well a long time ago. Maybe he owned all this land at one time. I just don't know. But we better talk to Sergeant Collins," Ricky's dad said.

They got up to the top of the hill.

"Come on. Let's all get in the car. We'll go over to see Sergeant Collins," Ricky's dad said.

CHAPTER 6

Sergeant Collins

They all got in the car. Ricky's dad turned the car around. Then they went down the old road. The police station was on Front Street.

"This old road is really a short cut," Ricky said.

"It isn't used very much. A lot of people forgot it was even here," Ricky's dad said.

They got to the police station. They all got out. Patches stayed in the car.

"We'll be back, Patches," Ricky said.

Sergeant Collins saw them walking in.

"Hello. What are all of you doing here?" the Sergeant asked.

"You tell him, Ricky," Ricky's dad said.

"Tom and I wanted to go fishing. We went up to the creek. It's the place we always go fishing. We didn't catch any fish. They were all dead. There was oil in the creek," Ricky said.

"Oil? In the creek?" the Sergeant said.

"That's right. We think it came from Mr. Stone's old well," Tom said.

"That couldn't be. There never was any oil in that old well," the Sergeant said.

"Maybe there really is some oil there," Ricky said.

"I have an idea. Let's all go out and see Mr. Stone's son. Mr. Stone is old. He lives with his son. His son can help us out," the Sergeant said.

Ricky's dad turned to Tom and Ricky. "You boys ride out with Sergeant Collins. I have to get back home."

"OK," Ricky said.

"See you later," Ricky's dad said. Then he left.

"Come on with me. We'll go in my police car," the Sergeant said.

Tom and Ricky got into Sergeant Collins' car. They went to Mr. Stone's house.

A man opened the door. "Can I help you?" he said.

"Can we talk to Mr. Stone?" the Sergeant asked.

"I'm Bob Stone, his son," the man said.

"I'm Bob Stone, his son," the man said.

Ricky looked at Bob Stone. "Wait. Don't you own Tim's gas station?" he asked.

"That's right. I thought I had seen you before," Bob said.

"Bob, can we see your father?" the Sergeant asked.

"He is very sick. He can't see anyone. What do you want?" Bob asked.

"Can you tell us anything about the old well?" the Sergeant asked.

"The old well? The old well up on the hill? Why?" Bob asked.

"There is oil going into the creek. It is killing the fish. We think it is coming from that old well," the Sergeant said.

"Oh, that. My father thought there might be oil there. But that was years ago. I didn't know anyone went near there anymore," Bob said.

"But there does seem to be oil coming from it," Ricky said.

"Maybe there is just a little. But it isn't much, I'm sure," Bob said.

"We wanted to talk to you first. We need to do something about it if there is oil there," the Sergeant said.

"I hope I've been able to help you," Bob said.

"Thank you for your time," the Sergeant said.

CHAPTER 7

Back to the Creek

Sergeant Collins took the boys back to Ricky's house. He let them off in front. Then he left to see what he could find out.

"What did Mr. Stone say?" Ricky's dad asked.

"We didn't see Mr. Stone. We saw Bob, his son. Bob owns the gas station," Ricky said.

"Is that right?" Ricky's dad said.

"Yes. Bob said he doesn't know anything about a lot of oil up at the well," Tom said.

"You know what? I want to go back to the creek. I want to look around some more," Ricky said.

"What do you think you'll find?" Tom asked.

"I don't know. I just want to look around that old well," Ricky said.

"You boys can go tomorrow. It's too late to go now," Ricky's dad said.

"Come on over tomorrow, Tom. We can ride over then," Ricky said.

The next day Tom met Ricky. They both got on their bikes. Patches barked. He wanted to go with them again.

"OK, Patches. Come on," Ricky said.

They got to the creek. They left their bikes in the same place they always did. Then they walked up the creek.

They started to look around.

"Look!" Tom called out.

"What is it?" Ricky said.

"There is a lot more oil coming down the hill," Tom said.

"Patches! Stop that," Ricky said. But Patches wouldn't stop.

"I hear something up the hill," Tom said.

"What do you think it is?" Ricky asked.

"I don't know," Tom answered.

"Let's go up and find out," Ricky said.

They ran up the hill.

"Look! Going down the road. It's a big red truck," Ricky said.

"Where?" Tom asked.

"You can't see it now. It just turned," Ricky said.

"A big red truck? What would it be doing here?" Tom asked.

"I don't know. Let's find out," Ricky said.

"Come on. Let's go back and get our bikes. We can go down the road. Maybe we'll see it again," Tom said.

They ran back down the hill. They got their bikes. Then they pulled them up the hill.

"Come on. Let's go down the old road," Ricky said.

The road was old. It had a lot of holes. No one used it anymore.

"Why did we have to go this way?" Tom asked.

The old road turned and turned. All of a sudden Tom said, "Look! There's Bob's gas station!"

"And look what's parked there! It's the big red truck I saw up by the well. It's the same one," Ricky said.

Tom and Ricky rode their bikes over to the truck. Ricky got off his bike. Then he got up on to the truck. There were four barrels on it.

"Well, what do you know?" Ricky said.

"What is it?" Tom asked.

"These are the same barrels that were here. We put my dad's old oil in one of them. But there's nothing in them now," Ricky said.

Bob came running over to Ricky. He looked mad.

Bob came running over to Ricky. "What are you doing up there?" he said. He looked mad.

"I was just looking in the barrels," Ricky said.

"Get off and get out of here," Bob yelled.

Ricky got off the truck. He got back on his bike.

"Come on, Tom. I think I know what all of this is about," Ricky said.

"I think I do, too," Tom said.

"Let's go back and see Sergeant Collins," Ricky said.

CHAPTER 8

Caught!

Tom and Ricky went back to the police station. Sergeant Collins saw them coming in. "What's up?" he asked them.

"We think we know all about the oil in that old well," Ricky said.

"Well, tell me. I've been trying to find out some things myself," the Sergeant said.

"My dad took some old car oil to Bob's gas station. There were a lot of barrels there. They were all full of old oil from cars," Ricky said.

"Go on," the Sergeant said.

"Today we saw a big red truck up by the well. We went to Bob's gas station. The barrels didn't have any oil in them," Ricky said.

"Do you mean Bob is putting oil in the well?" the Sergeant asked.

"Yes, we do," Tom said.

"Well, there's only one thing to do. We'll go out and talk to Bob. Come on," the Sergeant said.

"We'll meet you there. We'll go on our bikes," Ricky said.

Tom and Ricky got to Bob's gas station first. Then Sergeant Collins got there. Bob saw them coming.

"Bob, we need to talk to you again," the Sergeant said.

"Now what do you want?" Bob asked. He looked mad.

"Bob, are you putting oil in that old well?" the Sergeant asked.

"Why would I do that?" Bob asked.

"Tom and Ricky saw your red truck up by the well. More oil is coming out of the well," the Sergeant said.

"That truck has been here all day long," Bob said.

Just then a man came up to Bob. "I have some car oil to give you. I was here before. But you and the truck were not here," the man said.

"That's it, Bob. You better tell us everything," the Sergeant said.

Everyone looked at Bob.

"That's it, Bob. You better tell us everything."

"OK. OK. I was putting oil in that old well," Bob said.

"But why?" Ricky asked.

"My father owns the land where the well is. I wanted people to think there was oil there. That way I could sell it for a lot of money. That's why I bought this gas station from Tim. People bring a lot of old car oil here. I kept taking it up to the well," Bob said.

"Bob, I think you better come with me," Sergeant Collins said.

"Everything would have been all right. Those kids had to see the truck!" Bob said.

Bob went with Sergeant Collins to his car.

"Come on, Tom. Let's go," Ricky said.

Tom and Ricky got back to Ricky's house. They told Ricky's dad about Bob.

"The mystery of the oil is cleared up," Ricky's dad said.

Just then Ricky's mother came outside.

"When do we eat?" Ricky asked.

"I can't fix anything yet. Ricky, ride to the store and get me some cooking oil," she said.

Ricky's dad looked at her. "Cooking oil?"

"That's right. I can't cook without it," she said.

"Forget it. Let's all go and get a hamburger," Ricky's dad said.